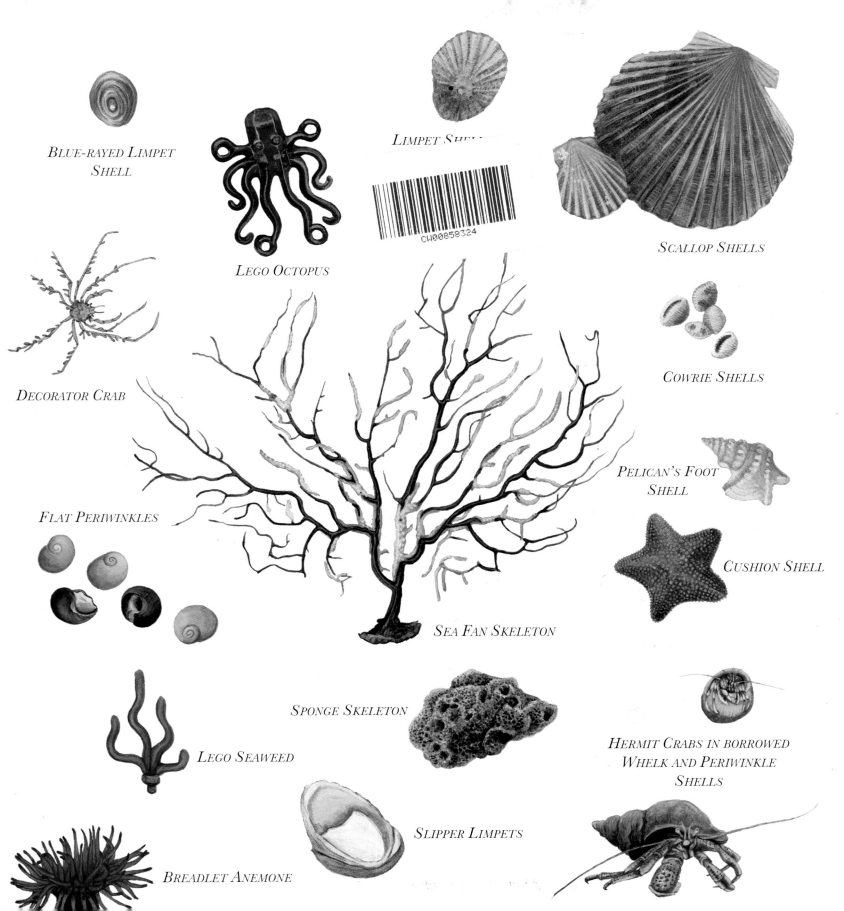

BLUE-RAYED LIMPET
SHELL

LEGO OCTOPUS

LIMPET SHELL

CW00858324

SCALLOP SHELLS

DECORATOR CRAB

COWRIE SHELLS

FLAT PERIWINKLES

PELICAN'S FOOT
SHELL

CUSHION SHELL

SEA FAN SKELETON

SPONGE SKELETON

LEGO SEAWEED

HERMIT CRABS IN BORROWED
WHELK AND PERIWINKLE
SHELLS

BREADLET ANEMONE

SLIPPER LIMPETS

First published in 2018 by
Mabecron Books Ltd
Briston Orchard, St Mellion, Saltash, Cornwall, PL12 6RQ
United Kingdom. All rights reserved.

Typeset in Baskerville
Printed in Italy

ISBN 978 09955 0284 0

Treasure from the Sea

Lisa Woollett
Illustrated by Sarah McCartney

Once there was a girl who liked to find things on the beach.

H er name was Ally and
under her bed she kept a box.

It was quite an ordinary box on the outside
but inside it was better than treasure.

It was a good collection because
children, like Ally, are good at looking,
and so they're good at finding.

Quite a lot of her finds were a mystery.

She did ask what things were sometimes, but it was surprising what grown ups didn't know.

Ally lived in Cornwall and often went to the beach with her friend Finn.

They swam
and skimmed stones,

jumped waves
and dripped wet sand into castle spires.

They made flat-stone towers and
sand angels with seaweed hair,

climbed rocks and dammed streams,
drew sea monsters in the sand with sticks.

When they went home, there was always something
in Ally's pocket for her collection.

Sometimes they saw a woman there.
She came to the beach in all weathers,
and was usually crouched down looking
at something.

They wandered towards her.
'Go on,' Finn said, 'Ask her what she's doing.'
'No!' Ally shoved him, 'You ask.'

For a while, the woman didn't seem to realise they were there. She had a bag with her, with plastic poking out.
Finn coughed, 'My friend, she was wondering ...'
She held something out towards them, 'I was looking at this.'
Finn shrugged, 'A dead crab?'
'It's not dead,' she said.
'Look. There are holes where the eyes should be.'

'A crab's hard shell means it can't grow,' she told them.
'So it grows a new, soft shell underneath. When it's ready,
the crab draws in seawater and swells up. The old shell
opens like a bin lid and the crab backs out. It leaves
behind this – a moult. Claws and all.'

The children took the crab and lifted the shell.
She was right. There was nothing inside.

MERMAID'S PURSE
CATSHARK

W hen they next saw her out at the
water's edge, Ally ran towards her. 'Come
on,' she called to Finn, 'She'll know.'
By the time Finn reached them,
Ally was pulling something
from her pocket.

'People call them mermaid's purses,'
the woman said.
'But they're really egg cases.
The ones with horns are laid
by a skate or ray, which is a fish
that has fins like wings.'
'That's my name,' she said. 'Rae.'

MERMAID'S PURSE
RAY

'The other kind are laid by the shark family.'
She described how the curly tendrils
anchor them to seaweed.

'Inside each egg case there's an embryo –
a tiny fish – that feeds off a yolk. After
many months, it swims out through an
opening at the bottom, here.'
She held it out to show them.

'Yours are empty,' she said. 'So they've
already hatched.'

On their trips to the beach they began to hope
they might see Rae.

One day they found her out on the rocks at low tide.
She showed them circles worn into the rock
and explained how every limpet has a home,
a round 'scar' it grinds to a perfect fit.

'At high tide the limpet heads out to graze underwater,
rasping food from the rocks with its saw-like tongue.
Then as the tide goes out, it follows its own mucus trail back home.'

DOG WHELKS

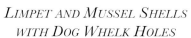

LIMPET AND MUSSEL SHELLS
WITH DOG WHELK HOLES

She showed them a limpet shell with a small hole.
'Evidence,' she said, 'that it has been eaten by a dog whelk.'

'A dog whelk glides up onto its victim
and drills through its shell.
Then it sucks its shellfish meal out through the hole like soup.'

LIMPET SCAR

FLAT PERIWINKLES

SAW WRACK

Sometimes Ally brought something
from the collection she kept under her bed,
in case they saw Rae.

One day it was her flat periwinkle shells. Rae
explained how the different colours meant they
could hide amongst different kinds of seaweed.

'Lots of sea creatures use camouflage,' she said.
'A decorator crab sticks seaweed to the velcro-like
hooks on its shell. And flatfish can change the colour
and pattern of their skin to match the seabed.'

BLADDERWRACK

DECORATOR CRAB

KNOTTED OR EGG WRACK

Beachcombing became one of the children's favourite things to do. Searching, wrecking, treasure hunting.

Twice a day the tide came in and twice a day it went out. Each high tide left a strandline across the beach.

Ally and Finn looked much more carefully now.
All along it, often hidden amongst seaweed,
were clues to secret worlds beneath the waves.

CUTTLEBONES

One windy autumn day, there were cuttlebones all along the strandline. Rae told them
this 'bone' was really an internal shell, used to
control how much the cuttlefish floats

or sinks.

OCTOPUS

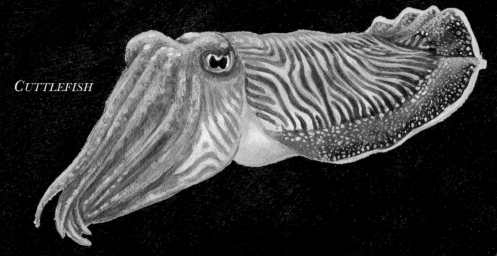

SQUID

'They are related to octopuses and squid,' she told them, 'and their family name means head foot.'

CUTTLEFISH

Rae said she sometimes found sea grapes, 'Cuttlefish eggs. The mother stains them black with her ink to protect them.'

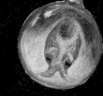

CUTTLEFISH EGGS

'If an egg misses the inking, you can see the baby cuttlefish growing inside.'

SPONGE SKELETON

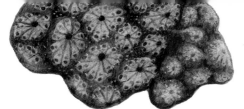

STAR SEA SQUIRT

BREADCRUMB SPONGE

That day, they also found sponges just like the ones people use in the bath. It turned out these were the skeletons of simple animals.

Rae told them that many sponges live in deeper water, where less sunlight reaches. 'There are some strange creatures down there like light-bulb sea squirts. And dead man's fingers!'
She grinned at the looks on their faces.
'It's ok, that's a kind of soft coral.'

'Have you ever found sea fans?' she asked them. The children had no idea.
'They look like twigs,' she said.
'But they're animals too.
I've got some up at the house.'
She waved towards the cliff path.

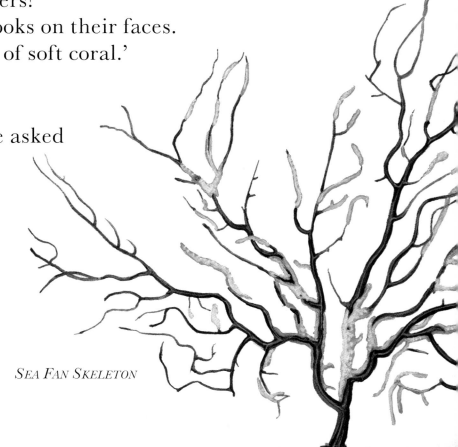

SEA FAN SKELETON

Later Rae told them about the Lego.
'Twenty years ago,' she said, 'a ship was hit by
a huge wave off Land's End. Five million pieces
of Lego were washed overboard and it still
washes up today.'

LEGO OCTOPUS

'There are Lego spear guns, cutlasses,
lifeboats, witches' brooms, seaweed,
divers' flippers and octopuses.'
She smiled at Finn's open mouth.
'And Lego dragons.'

'Where?' the children said together.
'You find it after storms, amongst other
washed-up plastic.' Rae looked sad.

LEGO DRAGON

'Plastic that gets into the ocean can be very
dangerous for wildlife. Creatures get trapped
or entangled in it, or mistake it for food and choke.
Seabirds feed pieces of plastic to their chicks.
It fills their stomachs and if they can't eat
enough real food to survive, they die.'

She patted the bag she carried.
'If you put even a few pieces in
the bin, it helps. And you
could be saving a life.'

PLANKTON SEEN
THROUGH A MICROSCOPE

Ally and Finn soon realised that even the most common things on the beach, like the barnacles on the rocks, had extraordinary lives.

Rae told them that the barnacles' young are tiny larvae that swim until they find a place to settle. 'They glue themselves headfirst to the rock and build volcano-shaped walls and a trapdoor.'

'When the tide comes in, the doors open and the barnacles wave feathery limbs to catch food.'

ACORN BARNACLES

One of the children's best finds was a driftwood log
covered in goose barnacles.

They learned that unlike the barnacles on the rocks,
the goose barnacles spend their whole life out at sea.
They attach to the flotsam (anything floating in the
ocean) by long rubbery necks that are called peduncles.

'When they washed up in the past,' Rae said,
'people sometimes thought they were sea monsters.'

BEADLET ANEMONE

SNAKELOCKS ANEMONES

CUSHION STAR

Although rockpools often seemed empty at first, Ally and Finn learned to look more carefully. They lifted seaweed, gently turned stones and sometimes found jewel-like treasures.

There were snakelocks anemones and starfish, and beadlet anemones that catch prey and fight for space with stinging cells that fire tiny harpoons.

When a shell moved suddenly, they often found a hermit crab inside as these have no shell of their own to protect them.

COMMON STARFISH

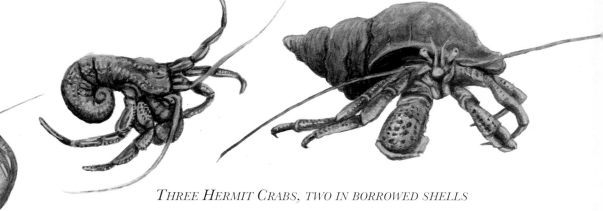

THREE HERMIT CRABS, TWO IN BORROWED SHELLS

One stormy day in winter, the beach was strewn with what looked like tiny cellophane sailboats. Ally and Finn waited a long time for Rae to arrive.

'By-the-wind sailors,' she told them at last. 'Thousands live together out at sea. These are their skeletons.'

She said they were related to the Portuguese man-o-war. This has a dangerous sting, she warned. 'If you see one you should never touch it.'

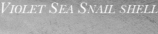
VIOLET SEA SNAIL SHELL

BY-THE-WIND SAILOR SKELETONS

VIOLET SEA SNAIL

PORTUGUESE MAN-O-WAR

It was then that she told them about the violet sea snail.
'It eats both of them,' Rae said. 'That's where it gets its beautiful colours.'

'It lives upside down at the water's surface, on a raft of bubbles it makes from its own mucus.
I've only ever found one.'

For a long time after that the children looked
for violet sea snails. Whenever they could they
came to the beach after storms and gales, and
hunted along the strandline.

They found many strange and beautiful things
for Ally's collection - there were three full boxes
under her bed now - but never a violet sea snail.
They decided the only way to see one would be
to visit Rae.

On an early spring day they set off along the
path she'd pointed out. As the track led up out
of the bushes, they stopped.
'That's got to be where Rae lives,' Ally said.
'That's her bag by the door'.
Finn whistled. 'She must have found all *this* on
the beach.'

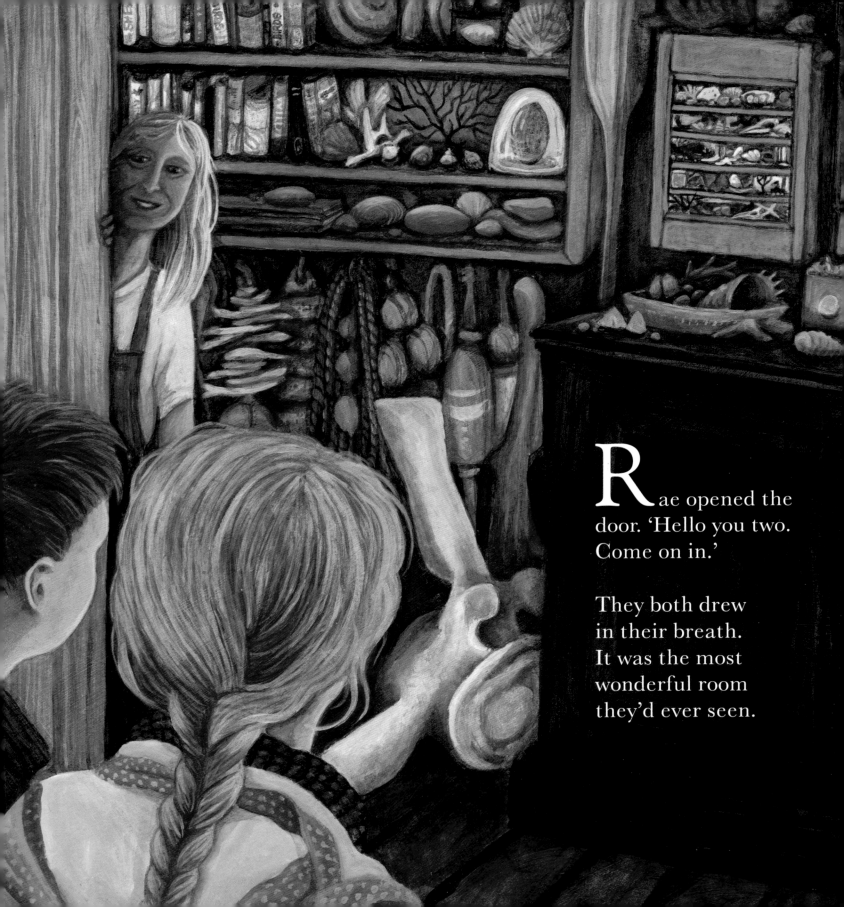

Rae opened the door. 'Hello you two. Come on in.'

They both drew in their breath. It was the most wonderful room they'd ever seen.

'My violet sea snail?' Rae grinned. 'Go on, see if you can find it. It might take a while. Remember to look for the sea fans ... and the Lego dragon!'

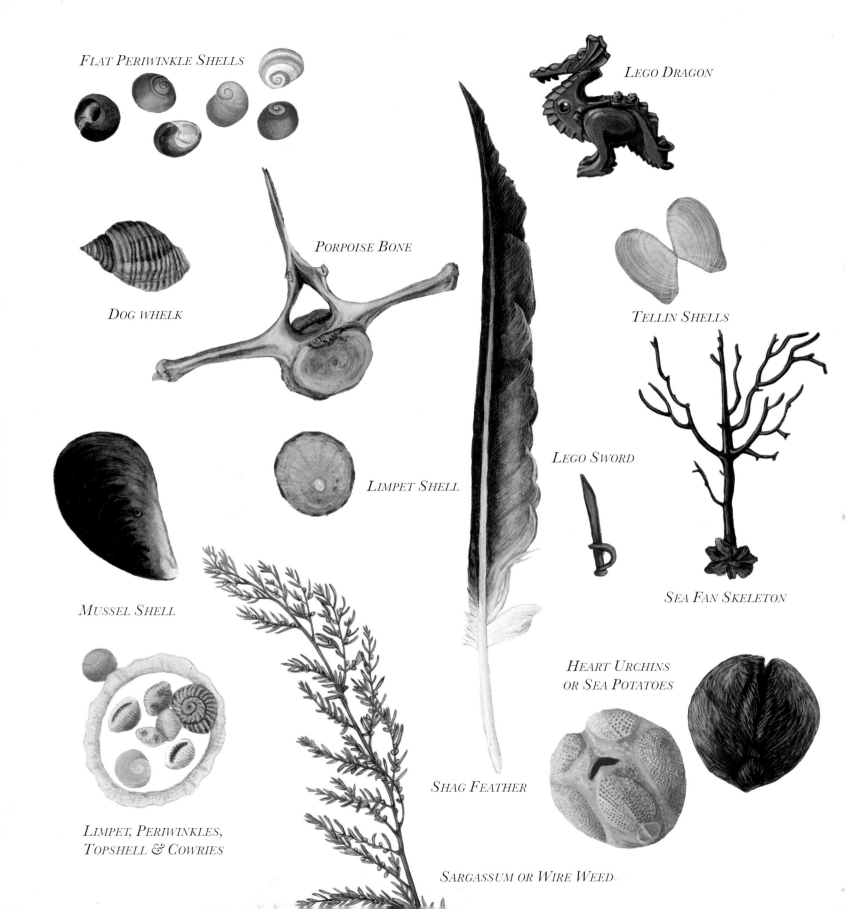

FLAT PERIWINKLE SHELLS

LEGO DRAGON

DOG WHELK

PORPOISE BONE

TELLIN SHELLS

LIMPET SHELL

LEGO SWORD

SEA FAN SKELETON

MUSSEL SHELL

HEART URCHINS
OR SEA POTATOES

LIMPET, PERIWINKLES,
TOPSHELL & COWRIES

SHAG FEATHER

SARGASSUM OR WIRE WEED